# The ABC Book

## Lyn Gray

with verses by Ian Souter

First published in 1996 by
Belair Publications Ltd.
P.O. Box 12, Twickenham, TW1 2QL,
England
© Illustrations Lyn Gray
© Verses Ian Souter
Editor Robyn Gordon
Printed in Singapore by Craft Print

ISBN 0 947882 98 7

Belair
Publications

# VOCABULARY

## Aa

**Nouns:** acrobat, alarm clock, anchors, animals, ankle, ants, apples, arrows, axe.
**Adjectives:** afraid, amazed, angry, annoyed, anxious, asleep.

## Bb

**Nouns:** baby, badge, bag, ball, balloon, bandage, bat, beak, bear, bed, bee, beetle, bell, belt, bicycle, bird, birthday cake, birthday cards, blackberry, blankets, boat, book, boomerang, boots, bottle, bow, box, boy, bricks, brushes, butterfly, button.
**Adjectives:** bad, black, blue, broken.
**Verbs:** to bounce, to burst.

## Cc

**Nouns:** cabbage, cactus, cage, cake, calendar, canary, candle, cap, card, carpet, carriage, carrots, castle, caterpillar, cats, cauliflower, clock, cloth, coach, collar, comb, cook, cow, cream, crowns, crumbs, crusts, cuff, cupboard, cups, currants, curtain, cushion.
**Adjectives:** cracked, curly.
**Verbs:** to cook, to crawl, to cut.

## Dd

**Nouns:** daffodils, daisies, dandelions, dartboard, darts, decorations, deer, diamond, dice, dinosaurs, dog, door handles, doors, donkeys, dots, dragon, drain, drainpipe, dress, dressing-gown, drum, drumsticks, ducks, dustbin.
**Adjective:** dark.
**Verbs:** to dance, to drink, to drip, to drum.

## Ee

**Nouns:** egg, eggcup, elbow, elephant, embroidery, emperor, engine, envelope, exhaust, explorers.
**Adjectives:** elaborate, elegant, eleven, enormous, exhausted, exploding, extravagant.
**Verbs:** to examine, to exercise, to explode.

## Ff

**Nouns:** face, fairy, farm, farmer, feather, feet, fence, fern, field, fin, fir cone, fish, flask, flies, flock, flowers, food, foot, fork, fox, foxgloves, freckles, frogs, fruit, fungus.
**Adjectives:** fat, five (flies), four (frogs), freckled.
**Verbs:** to float, to fly.

## Gg

**Nouns:** garden, gardener, gate, geese, ghost, girl, glass, gloves, goat, goose, gorilla, grapes, grass, grasshopper, greenhouse, ground, guinea-pig, gutter.
**Adjectives:** greedy, green (grass), grey (geese).
**Verbs:** to gasp, to glare, to gobble, to grab, to graze, to grin, to grow.

## Hh

**Nouns:** hammer, handbag, handkerchief, handle, harbour, hat, haystack, hearts, hedges, hedgehog, helicopter, helmet, hens, hill, hippopotamus, hive, holiday, hook, hoop, horn, horses, hose, houses.
**Adjectives:** happy, heavy, hungry.
**Verbs:** to hold, to hover.

## Ii

**Nouns:** igloo, injection, ink, insects, instruments, invalids.
**Adjectives:** injured, ill.
**Verb:** to imagine.
**Preposition:** in (bed).

## Jj

**Nouns:** jacket, jail, jam, jar, jelly, jewel, jewellery, jigsaw, jockey, jodhpurs, judge, jug.
**Adjective:** jolly.
**Verbs:** to join (pieces of jigsaw), to juggle.

## Kk

**Nouns:** kangaroo, kebab, keeper, kennel, ketchup, kettle, keys, kite, kitten, kiwi, koala.
**Verb:** to kiss.

## Ll

**Nouns:** lace, ladder, lady, ladybird, lamp, lantern, leaves, legs, leopard, letter, letterbox, library, librarian, light, lion, lighthouse, lips, lizard, lobster, lock, lollipop, lorry.
**Adjective:** little.
**Verbs:** to lean, to lend, to lick, to lift, to look.

## Mm

**Nouns:** magic, magician, magnet, man, map, marble, mask, matches, maze, medal, mermaid, mess, metal, mice, microscope, milk, milk bottle, mince pie, mirror, mole, money, money box, monkey, monster, moons, moth, mounds (earth), moustache, mouse, mouth, muddle, mug, mummy (Egyptian), mushrooms.
**Adjectives:** magic, magical.

## Nn

**Nouns:** nail, nappy, necklace, needle, nest, net, newspaper, night, night cap, nightdress, nightingale, nightshirt, notebook, notes (musical), noughts (and crosses), nurse, nuts.
**Adjectives:** nine (nuts, birds), noisy.

## Oo

**Nouns:** oblong, octopus, omelette, opera, orange, orange peel, ostrich, otter, ox.
**Verb:** to observe.

## Pp

**Nouns:** painting, paints, painter, panda, palace, paper, parcel, park, parrot, party, path, paw, pear, peel, pen, pencil, penguin, petal, petticoat, picnic, picture, piece (of pie), pie, pillars, pillow, pin, pineapple, pizza, plaits, plants, plates, playground, pocket, pond, ponytail, poppy, pram, present, princess, puppet, pyjamas.
**Adjectives:** pink, proud.
**Verbs:** to paint, to perch, to play, to point, to push.

## Qq

**Nouns:** queen, question mark, quill, quilt,
**Verbs:** to quack, to quarrel, to quieten.

## Rr

**Nouns:** rabbit, race, radio, rain, rainbow, raincoat, rat, reflection, reporter, ribbon, road, robber, robots, rock, rockets, roller skates, rope, rose, rucksack.
**Adjectives:** rapid, red.
**Verbs:** to read, to run, to rush.

## Ss

**Nouns:** sailor, sails, sand, sandals, sandcastle, sandwiches, sardines, saucepan, sausages, sea, seagull, seal, seaside, seashore, seaweed, sky, sleeve, slipper, snail, socks, spade, spider, starfish, stones, strap, submarine, suitcase, sun, sweets, swimmers.
**Adjectives:** seven (sausages), six (sardines), smiling, sparkling, spotted, striped, surprised.
**Verbs:** to shine, to splash, to swim.

## Tt

**Nouns:** table, tail, tambourines, tap, tea, teacup, teapot, teaspoon, tennis racket, tent, tiger, tin, tin opener, toad, toadstools, tomatoes, tools, torch, tracks, tractor, trailer, tray, tree, triangle, trombone, trousers, trumpets, tuba, tyres.
**Adjectives:** ten (travelling musicians), two (tubas, etc.).
**Verb:** to travel.

## Uu

**Nouns:** umbrella, underwear.
**Adjectives:** underground, upstairs.
**Verb:** to untie.
**Prepositions:** under, up.

## Vv

**Nouns:** vacuum cleaner, valley, van, vase, vegetables, vest, Viking, village, vine, violets, violin, volcano, vulture.

## Ww

**Nouns:** waistcoat, wall, washing, washing-line, washing-up bowl, washing-up liquid, wasp, watch, water, watering can, wheelbarrow, wind, windmill, windows, wings, woman, worm.
**Adjectives:** wey, white, windy, woollen (jumper).
**Verbs:** to watch, to water, to wink, to wipe, to wobble.

## Xx

**Nouns:** axe, box, fox, ox, saxophone, taxi.
**Adjectives:** six (boxes), exploding (boxes).
**Verb:** to explode.

## Yy

**Nouns:** yacht, yak, yogurt, yo-yo.
**Adjective:** yellow.

## Zz

**Nouns:** zebra, zebra crossing, zigzag, zip, zoo.

# INTRODUCTION

These ABC pictures are designed to heighten children's awareness of the sounds of the letters of the alphabet. They are also intended to develop language through discussion and observation.

Children will enjoy sharing the book with an adult. Visual detail can be explored together, and attention drawn to the sound of the letters by reading the verse. The verses add another dimension of humour and will encourage children to have fun with language, rhythm and rhyme.

Whenever possible, while talking about each picture with the child, link the picture or the letters with his or her own experience, for example, the initial letter of the child's name. You could play 'I Spy', asking for objects that begin with the given letter, or you could encourage the child to point to the letter on the page on hearing the same sound when you read the verse. It is important that children know that letters have sounds *and* names. They will need to know the alphabet, and alphabetical order - but at the same time will need to become aware of each letter's *sound* as well as its *name*.

A full list of vocabulary is given at the beginning of the book. The list includes nouns, adjectives and verbs. Some words may be considered too difficult, depending on a particular child's stage of development. However, less familiar words provide an opportunity to extend a child's vocabulary when appropriate.

You will notice that the page devoted to 'X' is different, because the letter is in the middle or at the end of the words illustrated. This provides a larger sample through which children can recognize the sound that 'X' most commonly makes. On the 'Q' page a queue is illustrated, but this is meant mainly as a visual joke, as of course the word does not have the usual 'qu' pronunciation. Some examples of blends and digraphs (for example, *sl* and *st* on the 'S' page, and *ch* on the 'C' page, etc.), have been included, and these can introduce another stage of phonic experience.

Most important of all is that the time spent together sharing this book should be enjoyable, should stimulate conversation and imagination, and provide an exciting stepping-stone on the path to independent reading.

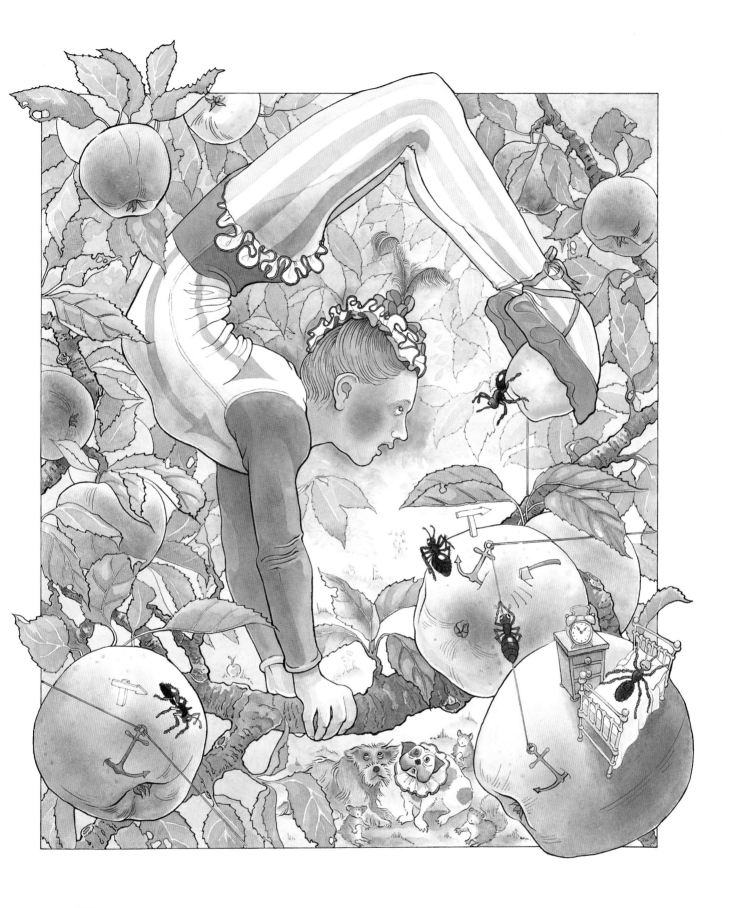

# Aa

Annie the acrobat climbed into a tree
And began picking apples as if they were free;
But an ant who was hungry and ready to dine
Arrived saying, 'Excuse me, this apple is MINE!'

# Bb

A baby with a bottle bounced on high,
Bursting a balloon as she tried to fly;
While below big brother just opened his eyes,
Wondering if this was his birthday surprise!

# Cc

Clara the cook was cutting with ease,
Carefully creating a cauliflower cheese,
Cheerfully chopping each piece with a crunch
Until a caterpillar called out, 'What's for lunch?'

# Dd

Dinky the Dinosaur was desperate to dance
With a dreamy-eyed dragon - it led to romance;
For they jived and they dived to a disco swing
And declared their love with a diamond ring.

# Ee

Three eager explorers whose jeep was overloaded,
Exhausted the engine until it exploded;
Then Ellie the Elephant strolled out of the greenery
With a letter to post - no time for machinery.

# Ff

When a friendly farmer flopped fast asleep,
Out flew a fairy to tickle and peep;
And while fuzzy, fat flies flip-flapped all around,
Frogs, fox and fish were firmly spellbound.

# Gg

A gardener and girl were carefully weeding
When Goat decided it was time for feeding;
So while geese got loose to guzzle and snatch,
A greedy gang gobbled up the vegetable patch.

# Hh

A holiday helicopter heavy with hippo,
Hovered, lost height and started to dippo;
Out went hammer, handbag and horn
Until, 'Hip, hip hooray!' once again - airborne.

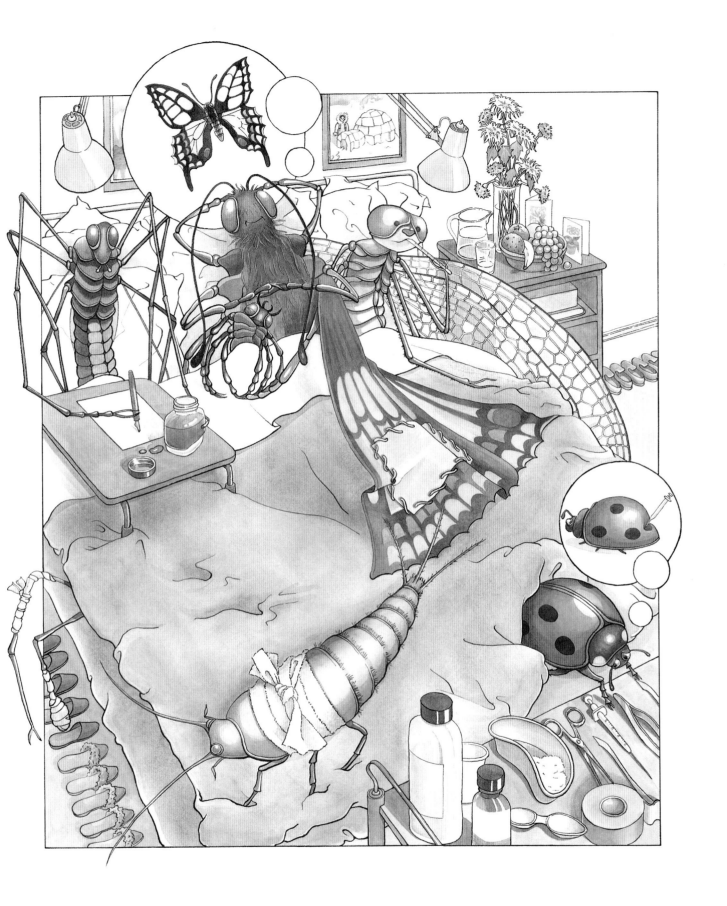

# Ii

Imagine lots of insects injured or ill,
Itchy and twitchy at having to lie still;
Where Butterfly dreams of being much better
And Daddy-long-legs scratches an inky letter.

# Jj

A jolly jockey was jiggling and juggling
With jelly and jewellery that he'd been smuggling;
When a joyless judge, called Justice Jack,
Jailed him, saying 'Give it all back!'

# Kk

When Kelvin the keeper fell asleep in a heap,
A kind kangaroo took a king-sized leap;
And with zing in his spring flew into the sky
Until bliss - a kiss with Miss Koala on high.

# Ll

Lion and Leopard worked in a library at night
While Ladybird searched for books by lamplight;
And Lizard, with lollipop, was seen by Miss Tut
Who politely announced, 'It's late - time to shut!'

# Mm

Melvin the Magician had an amazing surprise
When tricks became mixed in front of his eyes;
Where a mermaid appeared in a magical glow
And a mole in a hole said a friendly, 'Hello!'

# Nn

The Nightingales, at No. 9, just loved to sing,
So each night their nest would noisily swing;
While father took no notice, and just read the news,
Mother drifted off for a peaceful snooze.

An omelette-eating octopus was rather upset
When listening to an opera on his television set;
For an ox and an ostrich sounded very out-of-key,
While a rotter of an otter sang doh-ray-me!

# Pp

A princess from the palace stepped out with pride,
Pushing a pram with her panda inside;
Then without 'pardon' or 'please', and nose in the air,
She ploughed through a picnic as if it weren't there.

# Qq

Two queens in a queue were waiting for a bus;
They started to quarrel and started to fuss;
While the rest of the queue were quite taken aback,
Daphne the Duck was quick to say, 'QUACK!'

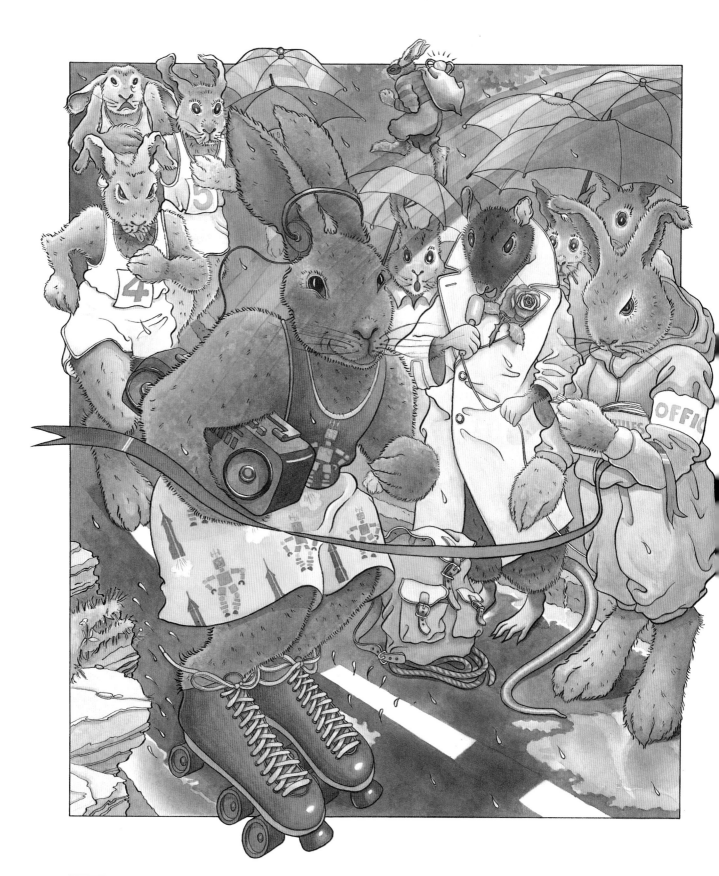

# Rr

A road-racing rabbit loved to run and run
But always came last, which wasn't much fun;
Until with red roller skates and his radio loud,
He raced round the track and surprised the crowd.

# Ss

A salty sailor who'd sailed the seven seas,
Dug up a suitcase, not treasure, if you please;
He found slippers and socks, but not a sign of gold,
And a string of soggy sausages, six days old.

# Tt

A tame but tired tiger lay asleep in a tree,
When a troupe of ten musicians arrived noisily,
With trombones and tubas making everything jump,
Poor old tiger's head was going bumpity-thump!

# Uu

The umbrellas pop open as a storm rumbles near,
But underground the animals have nothing to fear;
And while moles and worms head up for fresh air,
The badgers snuggle down without worry or care.

# Vv

A travelling Viking who used to like hiking,
Lived in a van, in a valley, to her liking,
Playing violin music, so soothing and light,
While Victor her vulture was dreaming of flight.

# Ww

On a wonderfully warm but windy morning,
A washing bowl topples without any warning;
And while Mr Flowers is watering a pot,
A worm can't decide if it's raining or not!

# Xx

A taxi with six boxes tied up on top,
Suddenly had to brake, suddenly had to stop;
While fox watched a box exploding on its own,
Ox just relaxed and played his saxophone.

# Yy

Listen everybody, here's something new,
It's the 'Yak Snack' - it's made just for you;
The mellow, yellow yogurt with lots of style,
Yes, one quick lick and you're sure to smile!

# Zz

A lively little zebra wanted a change of view,
So with the other zebras zigzagged out of the zoo;
But when a zip was unzipped there lay a surprise
For the lively little zebra was a child in disguise.

For details of further Belair Publications please write to
BELAIR PUBLICATIONS LTD
P.O. BOX 12, TWICKENHAM, TW1 2QL,
England

For sales and distribution (outside North and South America)
FOLENS PUBLISHERS
Albert House, Apex Business Centre,
Boscombe Road, Dunstable, Bedfordshire, LU5 4RL,
England

For sales and distribution in North America and South America
INCENTIVE PUBLICATIONS
3835 Cleghorn Avenue, Nashville, Tn 37215
U.S.A.

For sales and distribution Australia
EDUCATIONAL SUPPLIES PTY. LTD.
8 Cross Street, Brookvale, N.S.W. 2100
Australia